HMH |

Modules 3–4

Ways to Add and Subtract

MODULE 3 Properties of Operations

○ Build Understanding   ○ Connect Concepts and Skills   ○ Apply and Practice

MODULE 4 Apply the Addition and Subtraction Relationship

© Houghton Mifflin Harcourt Publishing Company • Image Credits: ©jtstewartphoto/iStock/Getty Images Plus/Getty Images; ©Nadezhda1906/Adobe Stock

⬤ Build Understanding   ⬤ Connect Concepts and Skills   ⬤ Apply and Practice

Properties of Operations

Symbol Search

Write +, −, or = to complete each equation.

1   7 (?) 1 = 6   7 ( ) 1 = 6

2   5 (?) 9 − 4   5 ( ) 9 − 4

3   8 = 3 (?) 5   8 = 3 ( ) 5

4   6 − 6 (?) 0   6 − 6 ( ) 0

5   10 (?) 7 (?) 3   10 ( ) 7 ( ) 3

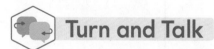 **Turn and Talk**

Explain what you did first to complete an equation. What did you do next?

Are You Ready?

Complete these problems to review prior concepts and skills you will need for this module.

Ways to Make 5

Use . Show different ways to make 5.
Color to show what you did.

1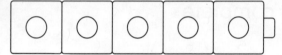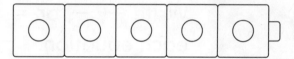

Use Symbols to Add

Use the picture. Write the addition equation.

2

Draw Equal Groups

Draw a circle below each picture to show an equal number of circles and birds.

3

Name _____

Represent Addition in Any Order

(I Can) use objects and draw to show that the sum stays the same when the order of the addends changes.

Spark Your Learning

Shawn and Janet build robots. All of their robots are either red or yellow. How can you add the robots?

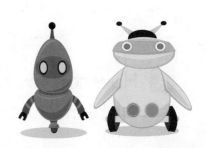

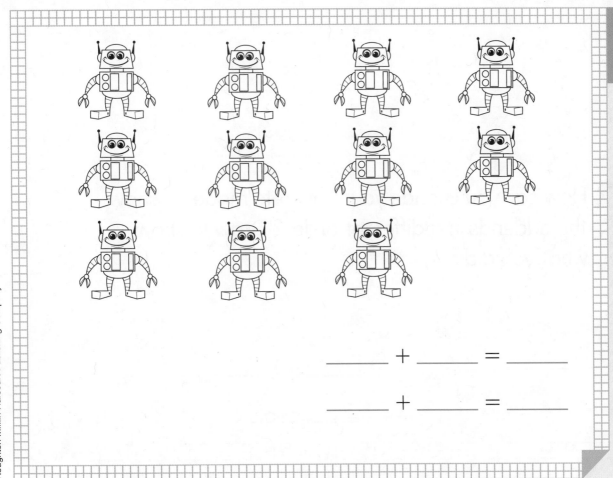

PAIRS

_____ + _____ = _____

_____ + _____ = _____

Ask children to color some of the robots red and some of the robots yellow. All the robots should be either red or yellow. Have children write an equation to show adding the red robots and the yellow robots. Then have children write an equation to add the yellow robots and the red robots. *What do you notice about the two sums?*

Module 3 • Lesson 1

Build Understanding

Paula scored 4 goals at the soccer game.
Cameron scored 2 goals at the soccer game.
How many goals did they score?

Connect to Vocabulary

Change the order of
the **addends**.

$8 + 9 = 17$

$9 + 8 = 17$

A How can you make a concrete model for the
problem? Draw to show what you did.

_____ + _____ = _____

_____ goals

B How can you change your concrete model to show
the addends in a different order? Draw to show
what you did.

_____ + _____ = _____

_____ goals

 Turn and Talk Why is the sum the same when
you change the order of the addends?

© Houghton Mifflin Harcourt Publishing Company

Lexi won 6 red ribbons and 5 blue ribbons at art shows. How many ribbons did she win?

A What two addition equations could you use to solve the problem? Show how to change the order of the addends.

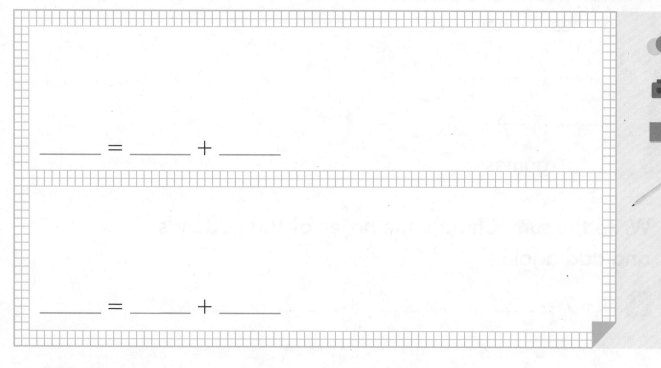

_____ = _____ + _____

_____ = _____ + _____

B Lexi won _____ ribbons.

. . . .

Check Understanding Math Board

Write two addition equations that can be used to solve the problem.

I Ron plants 3 white rose bushes and 9 red rose bushes. How many rose bushes does he plant?

_____ = _____ + _____

_____ = _____ + _____

_____ rose bushes

On Your Own

Write two addition equations that can be used to solve the problem. Draw pictures to match the equations.

2 Ⓜ️ **Reason** Mrs. Bank has 4 games. Mr. Moon has 5 games. How many games do they have?

_____ = _____ + _____

_____ = _____ + _____

_____ games

Write the sum. Change the order of the addends and add again.

3 9 + 7 = _____   ⋮   _____ + _____ = _____

4 _____ = 8 + 5   ⋮   _____ = _____ + _____

⬡ I'm in a Learning Mindset!

How did using objects help me understand how to add in any order?

_____

_____

Name _____

Add in Any Order

(I Can) show that when you change the order of
addends the sum stays the same.

Spark Your Learning

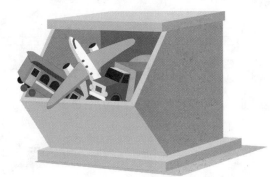

Toys in the Box		
Trucks	Planes	Trains
2	3	9

How many trucks and trains are there?

PAIRS

_____ + _____ or _____ + _____

_____ trucks and trains

*The table shows the number of toys in the toy box. How many trucks and trains
are there? Ask children to write two addition facts that can be used to solve
the problem. Allow children to choose tools. Have them choose a strategy to
use to solve the problem and draw to show what they did.*

Build Understanding

Kiki saw these butterflies on a bush.
How many butterflies did she see?

A What addition equation
   can you write?

   _____ + _____ = _____

   What strategy did you
   use to find the sum?

   _____

B Change the order of the
   addends. How can you
   show a different way
   to solve the problem?

   _____ + _____ = _____

   What strategy did you use?

   _____

C Kiki saw _____ butterflies.

 Turn and Talk Does it matter which of the two
equations you use to solve the problem? Explain.

© Houghton Mifflin Harcourt Publishing Company

Step It Out

▎1 How can one addition fact help you know another addition fact?

A What is 9 + 2?   **THINK:** Start at 9. Count on 2.

9, _____, _____

So, 9 + 2 = _____.

....

B If you know 9 + 2 = 11, what other addition fact do you know?

THINK: Change the order of the addends.

_____ + _____ = _____

 Turn and Talk Why might you want to change the order of the addends to add?

• •

Check Understanding Math Board

Write two addition equations that can be used to solve the problem.

▎1 There are 5 green apples and 6 red apples in a bag. How many apples are in the bag?

_____ + _____ = _____

_____ + _____ = _____

_____ apples

© Houghton Mifflin Harcourt Publishing Company

On Your Own

Write two addition equations that can be used to solve the problem.

2 (MP) **Use Repeated Reasoning**

Karen sees 7 red cars and 8 blue cars. How many cars does she see?

_____ = _____ + _____

_____ = _____ + _____

_____ cars

Write the sum. Change the order of the addends. Add again.

3 $5 + 3 =$ _____   _____ + _____ = _____

4 _____ $= 2 + 7$ _____ = _____ + _____

5 $6 + 7 =$ _____   _____ + _____ = _____

 I'm in a Learning Mindset!

Was I able to follow the directions? What part of the directions were not clear to me?

_____

© Houghton Mifflin Harcourt Publishing Company • Image Credits: ©Trimitrius/Shutterstock

Name

Represent Addition of 3 Numbers

(I Can) use objects and draw to show how to add three numbers.

Spark Your Learning

Amy sees a small garden with 6 tomato plants, 2 pepper plants, and 3 strawberry plants. How many plants are in the garden?

SMALL GROUPS

_____ plants

Read the problem aloud to children. Allow children to choose tools. Ask them to represent the problem with objects to find how many plants are in the garden. Have them draw to show what they did.

Build Understanding

Mrs. Smith uses 6 apples, 3 oranges, and 4 bananas in her fruit salad. Carla wants to know how many pieces of fruit Mrs. Smith uses.

$$6 + 3 + 4 = \boxed{}$$

Carla uses 6 , 3 , and 4  to show the problem.

A What addition fact does this show?

_____ + _____ = _____

B What is another concrete model Carla could use to find the sum?

_____ + _____ = _____

C Mrs. Smith uses _____ pieces of fruit.

Turn and Talk Why can you choose which two addends you add first?

Step It Out

1 There are 5 black pens, 2 red pens, and 4 blue pens on the desk. How many pens are on the desk?

A THINK: • Show each addend. $5 + 2 + 4 = \boxed{}$

• Group the two addends you will add first.

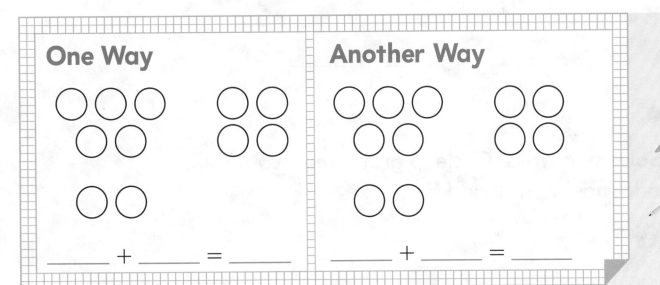

One Way

_____ + _____ = _____

Another Way

_____ + _____ = _____

B So, $5 + 2 + 4 =$ _____.

There are _____ pens on the desk.

Check Understanding

1 Steven draws a picture using 3 circles, 2 squares, and 1 triangle. How many shapes does he use?

_____ + _____ + _____ = _____

Steven uses _____ shapes.

On Your Own

Solve. Draw to show your thinking.

2 **MP Reason** Zoe sees 4 birds, 5 ducks, and 3 turtles at the lake. How many animals does she see?

_____

_____ + _____ + _____ = _____

_____ animals

Solve two ways. Circle to group the two addends you will add first.

3 2 + 5 + 3 = ☐

●● ●●●●● ●●●   ●● ●●●●● ●●●

_____ + _____ = _____   _____ + _____ = _____

So, 2 + 5 + 3 = _____.   So, 2 + 5 + 3 = _____.

+−×÷ I'm in a Learning Mindset!

What do I already know that can help me add three numbers?

_____

_____

Name _____

Add 3 Numbers

(I Can) use strategies to decide how to add three numbers.

Spark Your Learning

How can you use tools to show how to add 3 numbers?

____ + ____ + ____ = ▢

PAIRS

____ + ____ + ____ = ____

Have children choose three of the numbers shown at the top of the page and record them at the top of the workspace. Ask children to add the three numbers. Have them decide which two addends to add together first and draw to explain what they did.

Build Understanding

There are 6 bees at the front of the hive, 4 bees inside the hive, and 2 bees behind the hive. How many bees are at the hive?

A How can you use a strategy to group the addends in any order to solve the problem?

_____ + _____ = _____

So, $6 + 4 + 2 =$ _____.

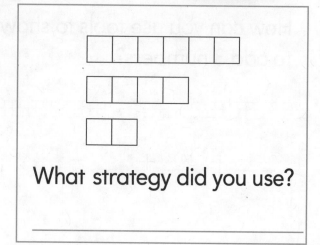

What strategy did you use?

_____

B How can you use a different strategy to group the addends in any order to solve the problem?

_____ + _____ = _____

So, $6 + 4 + 2 =$ _____.

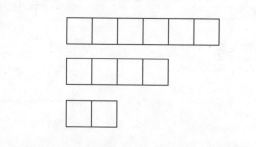

What strategy did you use?

_____

C There are _____ bees at the hive.

 Turn and Talk How can strategies help you choose which numbers to add first when there are three addends?

Step It Out

I ▷ $4 + 1 + 4 = $

A Here is one way you can solve the problem.

Count on. **THINK:** Start at 4. Count on 1.

$\textcircled{4} + \textcircled{1} + 4 = $ ▢   _____ + 4 = _____

B Here is another way to solve the problem.

Use doubles. **THINK:** $4 + 4$

$\textcircled{4} + 1 + \textcircled{4} = $ ▢   _____ + 1 = _____

C So, $4 + 1 + 4 = $ _____.

Check Understanding Math Board

Circle the two addends you decide to add first. Then solve.

I There are 3 birds in a tree. There are
5 birds in another tree. There are
2 birds on the ground. How many
birds are there?

$3 + 5 + 2 = $ ▢

_____ + _____ = _____

_____ birds

On Your Own

Solve.

2 (MP) **Reason** Michael reads 4 books.
Kay reads 3 books. Sam reads 6 books.
How many books do they read?

_____ books

- Explain how you chose which two addends
  to add first.

_____

_____

_____

**Solve two ways. Circle the addends you
add first.**

3 $6 + 3 + 3 =$ ▢

_____ + _____ = _____

$6 + 3 + 3 =$ ▢

_____ + _____ = _____

⬡ I'm in a Learning Mindset!

When adding $6 + 3 + 3$ two ways, which way worked
better for me? Why?

_____

_____

© Houghton Mifflin Harcourt Publishing Company • Image Credits: ©mitgirl/Adobe Stock

Keep Going ▶ Practice and Homework Journal

Name _____

Add 3 Numbers to Solve Problems

(I Can) find the sum of three numbers to solve
word problems.

Step It Out

1 A plant has 5 leaves at the top, 2 leaves
in the middle, and 1 leaf at the bottom.
How many leaves does the plant have?

A Use objects to show the problem.

THINK: I can connect cubes
to show each addend.

B Group the two addends you will add first.
Draw to show what you did.

_____ + _____ = _____

C Write to solve the problem.

_____ + _____ + _____ = _____

The plant has _____ leaves.

Step It Out

2 Joe has 2 cats. Dawn has 2 cats. Sandy has 6 cats. How many cats do they have altogether?

Decide which addends you will add together first.

A Here is one way. **THINK:** Add doubles.

2 + 2 + 6 = ☐

_____ + _____ = _____

B Here is another way. **THINK:** Count on 2.

2 + 2 + 6 = ☐

_____ + _____ = _____

C Joe, Dawn, and Sandy have _____ cats.

Check Understanding [Math Board]

Solve. Draw to show your work.

1 There is 1 deer, 3 rabbits, and 7 birds at the pond. How many animals are at the pond?

_____ animals

On Your Own

Solve. Draw or write to show your thinking.

2 (MP) **Reason** Bashir sees 2 striped kites,
I red kite, and 3 blue kites in the sky.
How many kites does he see?

_____ kites

3 (MP) **Reason** Cole has 5 green marbles,
4 red marbles, and 5 purple marbles.
How many marbles does he have?

_____ marbles

4 (MP) **Model with Mathematics** Paul, Vicki,
and Beth each scored 3 goals at soccer
practice. How many goals did they score?
Complete the equations to solve.

_____ + _____ + _____ = ▢

_____ + _____ = _____

_____ goals

On Your Own

Solve.

5 Sam stacks 8 large boxes, 2 medium boxes, and 1 small box. How many boxes does she stack?

_____ boxes

---

6 Tonya has 4 stamps from countries in Asia, 5 stamps from countries in Africa, and 1 stamp from a country in Europe. How many stamps does she have?

_____ stamps

---

7 (MP) **Reason** Find the unknown addend. Complete the equation.

$1 + 3 + \boxed{} = 5$

$1 + 3 + \underline{} = 5$

---

8 **Open Ended** Write and solve a word problem that adds 3 numbers.

_____

_____

_____ = _____ + _____ + _____

Name _____

Determine Equal and Not Equal

(I Can) draw and write to show whether an equation is true or false.

Step It Out

1 How can you use objects to show that this equation is true?

$$10 - 6 = 2 + 2$$

A
Draw to show $10 - 6$.	Draw to show $2 + 2$.

B Solve each side of the equation.

$10 - 6 =$ _____ and $2 + 2 =$ _____.

C Are both sides equal?   Yes   No

D Is the equation true?   Yes   No

Step It Out

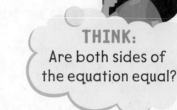

2 ▶ Is this equation true or false?

$$5 + 1 = 9 - 4$$

A Find the difference or sum on both sides of the equation.

$5 + 1 = $ _____ and $9 - 4 = $ _____.

B Are both sides equal? _____

C Is the equation true or false? _____

---

3 ▶ Is this equation true or false?

$$4 + 3 + 1 = 6 + 2$$

A Find the sum on both sides of the equation.

$4 + 3 + 1 = $ _____ and $6 + 2 = $ _____.

B Are both sides equal? _____

C Is the equation true or false? _____

---

4 ▶ Circle the equations that are true.

$3 + 5 = 8 + 1$ $6 - 2 = 1 + 3$ $8 = 10 - 2$

$9 - 2 = 4 + 3$ $7 + 3 = 2 + 6$ $12 = 12$

Step It Out

Find the number to make the equation true.

5 $3 + 5 = \boxed{} + 3$

A Show your thinking. Draw to complete the visual model.

$\blacksquare\blacksquare\blacksquare + \blacksquare\blacksquare\blacksquare\blacksquare\blacksquare = \boxed{} + \blacksquare\blacksquare\blacksquare$

B Write the number that makes the equation true.

$$3 + 5 = \underline{} + 3$$

Check Understanding Math Board

I Is the equation true or false? Circle your answer. Draw to show how you know.

$2 + 3 = 1 + 4$ True   False

On Your Own

MP **Reason** Is the equation true or false?
Circle your answer. Draw to show how
you know.

2 $7 + 1 = 4 + 4$ True False

3 $6 - 2 = 0 + 4$ True False

MP **Attend to Precision** Circle True or False.

4 $7 + 3 = 9 + 1$ True False

5 $6 = 11 - 4$ True False

6 $2 + 5 = 9 - 3$ True False

7 $1 + 2 + 6 = 3 + 6$ True False

8 (MP) **Construct Arguments** Michael wrote
$6 + 7 = 10 - 3$. He made a mistake.

A Explain the mistake Michael made.

_____

_____

B How could you make the equation true?

_____

_____

Write the number to make each equation true.

9 $6 = $ _____

10 $4 + 8 = $ _____ $+ 4$

11 _____ $+ 1 = 2 + 2$

12 _____ $- 1 = 9 - 7$

13 $10 - $ _____ $= 4 + 3$

14 $6 + $ _____ $= 2 + 3 + 1$

15 $4 = $ _____ $- 9$

16 _____ $+ 5 = 2 + 9$

17 **Open Ended** Write numbers to make each
equation true.

_____ $+ 6 = 1 + $ _____

$5 + $ _____ $= 8 - $ _____

On Your Own

18 Look at the equation. Use the same numbers.
Write a different equation that is true.

$$6 + 7 = 13$$

_____ = _____ ◯ _____

---

19 (MP) **Reason** Use two cards to write an equation
that is true.

| $3 + 9$ | $9 - 3$ | $8 + 4$ |

| $4 + 10$ | $12 - 9$ |

_____ ◯ _____ = _____ ◯ _____

---

20 (MP) **Reason** Use two cards to write an equation
that is true.

| $9 - 2$ | $3 + 5$ | $2 + 3 + 4$ |

| $4 + 4 + 2$ | $15 - 6$ |

_____ ◯ _____ ◯ _____ = _____ ◯ _____

Keep Going to▶ Practice and Homework Journal

Name _____

Develop Fluency in Addition

(I Can) quickly solve addition facts within 10.

Step It Out

1 Toby tosses two number cubes. What is the sum of his numbers?

A Add. Write to match how the cubes are shown.

B Add. Write to match how the cubes are shown.

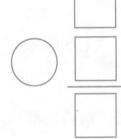   

C Compare the two sums. Are they the same? Circle your answer.

The sums are / are not the same.

D The sum of his two numbers is _____.

Step It Out

2 Gwen has 8 goldfish. Juan gives her 1 more. How many goldfish does Gwen have now?

A Write the addition one way.

B Write the addition another way.

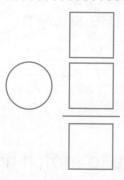

C Gwen has _____ goldfish.

Check Understanding [Math Board]

Solve. Write the addition two ways.

1 6 bees are in the garden. 3 bees join them. How many bees are in the garden now?

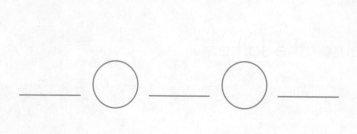 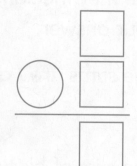

There are _____ bees in the garden now.

On Your Own

Solve.

2  **MP Use Structure** Joyce sees 4 ladybugs on one leaf and 3 ladybugs on another leaf. How many ladybugs does she see?

_____ ◯ _____ ◯ _____

_____ ladybugs

3 **MP Use Structure** 6 ducks are in the pond. 2 ducks join them. How many ducks are in the pond now?

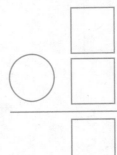

_____ ducks

4 **Open Ended** Write three different ways to add to make 10.

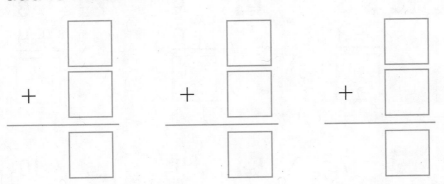

Add.

5 $3 + 5 =$ _____   **6** $4 + 5 =$ _____   **7** $1 + 7 =$ _____

On Your Own

Add.

8 $\begin{array}{r} 2 \\ +6 \\ \hline \end{array}$	**9** $\begin{array}{r} 3 \\ +3 \\ \hline \end{array}$	**10** $\begin{array}{r} 1 \\ +7 \\ \hline \end{array}$	**11** $\begin{array}{r} 5 \\ +4 \\ \hline \end{array}$
12 $\begin{array}{r} 5 \\ +1 \\ \hline \end{array}$	**13** $\begin{array}{r} 9 \\ +1 \\ \hline \end{array}$	**14** $\begin{array}{r} 0 \\ +5 \\ \hline \end{array}$	**15** $\begin{array}{r} 1 \\ +6 \\ \hline \end{array}$
16 $\begin{array}{r} 5 \\ +5 \\ \hline \end{array}$	**17** $\begin{array}{r} 1 \\ +5 \\ \hline \end{array}$	**18** $\begin{array}{r} 7 \\ +3 \\ \hline \end{array}$	**19** $\begin{array}{r} 8 \\ +1 \\ \hline \end{array}$
20 $\begin{array}{r} 2 \\ +4 \\ \hline \end{array}$	**21** $\begin{array}{r} 5 \\ +3 \\ \hline \end{array}$	**22** $\begin{array}{r} 9 \\ +0 \\ \hline \end{array}$	**23** $\begin{array}{r} 3 \\ +4 \\ \hline \end{array}$
24 $\begin{array}{r} 3 \\ +7 \\ \hline \end{array}$	**25** $\begin{array}{r} 7 \\ +2 \\ \hline \end{array}$	**26** $\begin{array}{r} 4 \\ +4 \\ \hline \end{array}$	**27** $\begin{array}{r} 10 \\ +0 \\ \hline \end{array}$

Keep Going ▶ Practice and Homework Journal

Module 3 Review

Vocabulary

Use the equation to answer the questions.

1 Circle the addends.

$$3 + 7 = 10$$

2 Write the equation with the addends in a different order.

_____ + _____ = _____

Concepts and Skills

Fill in the bubble next to the addition that can be used to solve the problem.

3 Jared sees 5 stars in the sky. Then he sees 4 more. How many stars does Jared see now?

○ $\begin{array}{r} 5 \\ + 4 \\ \hline 9 \end{array}$ ○ $\begin{array}{r} 4 \\ + 4 \\ \hline 8 \end{array}$ ○ $\begin{array}{r} 5 \\ + 5 \\ \hline 10 \end{array}$

4 Kiaya has 2 red bows and 5 purple bows. How many bows does Kiaya have?

○ $2 + 3 = 5$ ○ $5 + 2 = 7$ ○ $3 + 5 = 8$

5 Janet has 3 toy cars and 6 toy trucks.
To find the number of toy cars and trucks,
she uses $3 + 6 = 9$. What other equation
can she use?

_____ + _____ = _____

6 Mike adds $6 + 4 + 3$. Show two ways he
might solve the problem. Circle the addends
you add first.

$6 + 4 + 3 = \boxed{}$ | $6 + 4 + 3 = \boxed{}$

_____ + _____ = _____ | _____ + _____ = _____

So, $6 + 4 + 3 =$ _____. | So, $6 + 4 + 3 =$ _____.

7 Carl sees 2 birds in a nest. He sees 1 bird
on the ground. He sees 3 birds in the sky.
How many birds does Carl see?

_____ birds

8 Is the equation true or false? Fill in the
bubble to answer.

	True	False
$7 - 2 = 4 + 1$	○	○
$1 + 8 = 5 + 5$	○	○

Apply the Addition and Subtraction Relationship

Bird Nest Math

Find each unknown sum or difference. Write a sum on the nest. Write a difference on the bird.

Color the sums . If both birds show doubles, color them .
Color the rest of the birds .

Turn and Talk

What strategies did you use?
Give an example to explain.

Are You Ready?

Complete these problems to review prior concepts and skills you will need for this module.

Add Within 5

Use 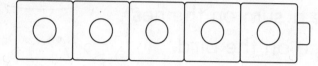 to show the equation.
Color to match. Write the sum.

1

$2 + 3 =$ _____

$3 + 2 =$ _____

Count On

Count on to add. Write the sum.

2 $6 + 1 =$ _____

3 $7 + 2 =$ _____

4 $9 + 3 =$ _____

Count Back

Count back to subtract. Write the difference.

5 $7 - 3 =$ _____

6 $11 - 2 =$ _____

7 $8 - 1 =$ _____

Name _____

Think Addition to Subtract

(**I Can**) use addition to help solve a subtraction problem.

Spark Your Learning

Jamel has 13 pears.
8 are yellow. The rest are green.
How can you use addition to find
how many green pears he has?

Math Board

PAIRS

Jamel has _____ green pears.

Read the problem aloud. Have pairs of children work together to show how to
solve the problem.

Build Understanding

There are 9 frogs at the pond.
4 of the frogs swim.
The rest sit on a log.
How many frogs sit on the log?

$9 - 4 = $ ◻

A How can you show the problem as addition?

B How can you write an addition equation
to help you solve the subtraction equation?

_____ + _____ = _____

So, $9 - 4 =$ _____.

C _____ frogs sit on the log.

 Turn and Talk What do you notice about the
addition and subtraction equations you used to
solve the problem?

© Houghton Mifflin Harcourt Publishing Company

Step It Out

1 7 girls play basketball.
3 of them wear green.
The rest wear blue.
How many girls wear blue?

A There are 7 girls altogether.

THINK: The number I subtract from is _____.

....

B 3 of the girls wear green.

THINK: The number I subtract is _____.

....

C Use an addition fact to help you
subtract $7 - 3 = $ [ ].

THINK: What number added to 3 makes 7?

$3 + $ _____ $= 7$

....

D So, $7 - 3 = $ _____.

....

E _____ girls wear blue.

Turn and Talk What do you notice about the
number 7 in the addition equation and the
subtraction equation?

Step It Out

2 There are 13 birds in a tree.
9 are red. The rest are blue.
How many blue birds are in the tree?

Use addition to solve $13 - 9 = $ ☐.

A Use the numbers from the subtraction
equation to write an addition equation.

$9 + $ ☐ $ = 13$

What number added to 9 makes 13? _____

$9 + $ _____ $ = 13$

So, $13 - 9 = $ _____.

B _____ blue birds are in the tree.

Check Understanding

Write an addition equation to help you subtract.

1 Anthony picks 11 flowers.
8 of them are red. The rest are pink.
How many pink flowers does he pick?

_____ $+$ _____ $=$ _____

$11 - 8 = $ _____   _____ pink flowers

On Your Own

(MP) Model with Mathematics Write an addition equation to help you subtract.

2 Cristian has 14 marbles. 6 are purple. The rest are green. How many green marbles does Cristian have?

_____ + _____ = _____

14 – 6 = _____

_____ green marbles

3 There are 8 bugs. 3 are on a leaf. The rest of them are on a stick. How many bugs are on a stick?

_____ + _____ = _____

8 – 3 = _____

_____ bugs

4 There are 13 plants in the garden. 7 are short. The rest are tall. How many tall plants are in the garden?

_____ + _____ = _____

13 – 7 = _____

_____ tall plants

On Your Own

5 (MP) **Reason** Explain how you can use an addition equation to help you subtract $12 - 7$.

_____

_____

_____

Write an addition equation to help you subtract.

6 What is $11 - 2$?

_____ + _____ = _____

So, $11 - 2$ = _____ .

7 What is $12 - 4$?

_____ + _____ = _____

So, $12 - 4$ = _____ .

8 What is $16 - 7$?

_____ + _____ = _____

So, $16 - 7$ = _____ .

9 What is $17 - 9$?

_____ + _____ = _____

So, $17 - 9$ = _____ .

➕✖️➗ I'm in a Learning Mindset!

How did I feel about my learning when I used addition to help me subtract?

_____

_____

Keep Going to▶ Practice and Homework Journal

Name _____

Represent Related Facts

(I Can) represent related facts in different ways.
I can use related facts to find unknown numbers.

Spark Your Learning

There are 13 sailboats.
8 sailboats have striped sails.
The other 5 have white sails.
How can you write an addition
equation about the sailboats?
How can you write a subtraction equation?

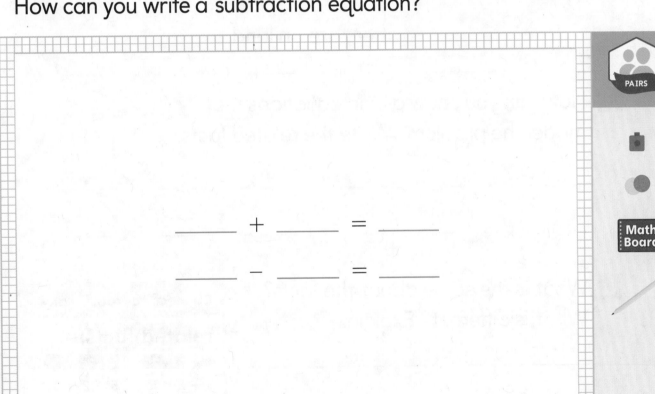

_____ + _____ = _____

_____ − _____ = _____

Read the problem to children. Have pairs choose tools and work together to
show how to write an addition fact and a subtraction fact about the sailboats.

Build Understanding

There are 14 otters. 6 of them are in the water. The rest are on land. How many otters are on land?

A How can you use a concrete model to show the otters?

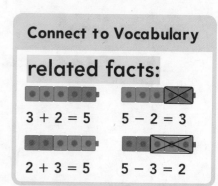

_____ otters are on land.

B How can you show all the equations that model the problem? Write the related facts.

_____ + _____ = _____   _____ − _____ = _____

_____ + _____ = _____   _____ − _____ = _____

C What is the same about the facts? What is different? Explain.

_____

_____

_____

Connect to Vocabulary

related facts:

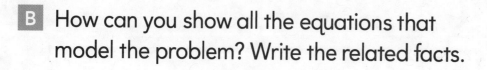

3 + 2 = 5   5 − 2 = 3

2 + 3 = 5   5 − 3 = 2

 Turn and Talk How did your concrete model help you write the related facts?

Name _____

Step It Out

1 How can you use 🔲🔲 to complete the related facts? Draw to show your work.

$$9 + \boxed{} = 11 \qquad 11 - 2 = \boxed{}$$

$$2 + 9 = \boxed{} \qquad \boxed{} - \boxed{} = \boxed{}$$

A Show the two addition facts.

THINK: Show the addends in a different order.

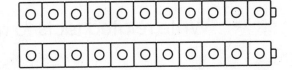

B Show the two subtraction facts.

THINK: Start with 11 🔲. Take away 2 or 9.

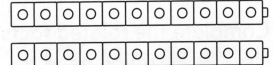

C Use your 🔲🔲 to complete the related facts.

$$9 + \underline{\qquad} = 11 \qquad 11 - 2 = \underline{\qquad}$$

$$2 + 9 = \underline{\qquad} \qquad \underline{\qquad} - \underline{\qquad} = \underline{\qquad}$$

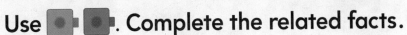

Check Understanding [Math Board]

Use 🔲🔲. Complete the related facts.

1 $7 + \underline{\qquad} = 12$ $\qquad\qquad$ $12 - \underline{\qquad} = 7$

$5 + \underline{\qquad} = 12$ $\qquad\qquad$ $\underline{\qquad} - \underline{\qquad} = \underline{\qquad}$

© Houghton Mifflin Harcourt Publishing Company

On Your Own

2 (MP) **Model with Mathematics**

Becca has 13 stickers.

7 of them are dog stickers.

The rest are cat stickers.

How many cat stickers does she have?

_____ cat stickers

- Write related facts to model the problem.

_____ + _____ = _____   _____ − _____ = _____

_____ + _____ = _____   _____ − _____ = _____

Complete the related facts.

Use 🔲🔲 **if you need to.**

3   3 + 9 = _____   12 − _____ = 9

9 + _____ = 12   _____ − _____ = _____

4   4 + _____ = 11   11 − 4 = _____

_____ + _____ = _____   11 − 7 = _____

🔳 I'm in a Learning Mindset!

What did I learn from the way others used related facts to find unknown numbers?

_____

© Houghton Mifflin Harcourt Publishing Company • Image Credits: DIvector/Dreamstime

Name _____

Identify Related Facts

(I Can) tell when addition and subtraction facts are related to each other.

Spark Your Learning

How can you use the same numbers to show related addition and subtraction facts?

Me: _____   My Partner: _____

○ ───   ───   ○ ───

○ ───   ───   ○ ───

○ ───   ───   ○ ───

○ ───   ───   ○ ───

PAIRS

Math Board

Have each child and a partner choose a number from 0 to 10 and write their numbers at the top of the page. Then have them use their numbers to help write four related addition and subtraction facts. Allow partners to choose a tool to help them write the related facts.

Build Understanding

ACTIVITY

There are 15 butterflies in the garden.
9 are blue. The other 6 are orange.

A How can you use a concrete model
to show the butterflies?

B How can you use your concrete model to
write two related facts about the butterflies?

C How do you know the facts are related?

_____

_____

Turn and Talk What other related facts can
you write using the same numbers?

Step It Out

1 What related facts does the picture show?

A Write how many.

_____   _____

_____ and in all

B Complete the facts.
Circle the related facts.

$6 + 4 =$ _____ $10 - 4 =$ _____ $10 + 4 =$ _____

2 Complete the facts.
Circle the facts if they are related.

THINK: Related facts use the same 3 numbers.

$17 - 9 =$ _____ $8 + 9 =$ _____

Check Understanding Math Board

Solve. Then circle the pairs that are related facts.

1 $8 + 5 =$ _____

$13 - 8 =$ _____

2 $3 + 7 =$ _____

$11 - 7 =$ _____

On Your Own

3 (MP) **Reason** 9 turtles are at the pond.
7 of them are on the sand.
The other 2 are in the water.
Circle two related facts about the turtles.

$2 + 7 = 9$ $9 + 7 = 16$ $9 - 7 = 2$

Solve. Then circle the pairs that are related facts.

4 $7 + 8 =$ _____
$7 - 3 =$ _____

5 $14 - 9 =$ _____
$14 - 5 =$ _____

6 $8 + 8 =$ _____
$16 - 8 =$ _____

7 $4 + 9 =$ _____
$10 - 5 =$ _____

8 $7 + 5 =$ _____
$7 - 5 =$ _____

9 $6 + 8 =$ _____
$14 - 6 =$ _____

 I'm in a Learning Mindset!

How does the way my group feels about
finding related facts affect my learning?

_____

Name

Use Addition to Check Subtraction

(I Can) use a related addition fact to check the answer to a subtraction problem.

Spark Your Learning

Martina has 11 fruits. 8 are mangos. The rest of the fruits are pineapples. How can you use related facts to find how many pineapples she has?

PAIRS

Math Board

_____ – _____ = _____

_____ + _____ = _____

Martina has _____ pineapples.

Read the problem aloud. Have pairs of children choose tools to show the problem as addition and subtraction. Children should write related addition and subtraction facts that can be used to solve the problem.

Build Understanding

13 children play sports after school.
6 of them play soccer. The rest play basketball.
How many children play basketball after school?

A How can you show the problem?

B How can you write a subtraction
equation to model the problem?

_____ − _____ = _____

C _____ children play basketball after school.

D How can you write an addition
equation to check your subtraction?

_____ + _____ = _____

 Turn and Talk How does adding help you
check subtraction?

Step It Out

1. 17 animals are in the park.
8 are squirrels. The rest are skunks.
How many skunks are in the park?

A Subtract to solve. Use any strategy.

$17 - 8 = $ _____

B Write a related addition fact
to check your subtraction.

THINK: Use the same 3 numbers.

_____ + _____ = _____

C There are _____ skunks in the park.

Check Understanding Math Board

Subtract. Then add to check your answer.

1. Benny sees 16 dogs.
8 of them are young.
The rest are old.
How many dogs are old?

$16 - 8 = $ _____

_____ + _____ = _____

_____ old dogs

2. $13 - 9 = $ _____

_____ + _____ = _____

3. $11 - 5 = $ _____

_____ + _____ = _____

On Your Own

Subtract. Then add to check your answer.

4 **Open Ended** Dan builds 10 sandcastles.
Some are small, and some are big.
How many big sandcastles could he build?

10 – _____ = _____

_____ + _____ = _____   _____ big sandcastles

---

5 (MP) **Model with Mathematics**
Melissa has 16 crayons.
7 are blue. The rest are red.
How many crayons are red?

16 – 7 = _____

_____ + _____ = _____   _____ red crayons

---

6 12 – 4 = _____   **7** 11 – 8 = _____

_____ + _____ = _____   _____ + _____ = _____

I'm in a Learning Mindset!

How do I feel when I am learning something
new or learning something a different way?

_____

© Houghton Mifflin Harcourt Publishing Company • Image Credits: ©Nadezhda1906/Adobe Stock

Name _____

Use Subtraction to Find an Unknown Addend

(I Can) use a related subtraction fact
to find an unknown addend.

Spark Your Learning

Trina has 7 purple flowers.
Robert has some yellow flowers.
They have 12 flowers altogether.
How many yellow flowers
does Robert have?

Math Board

_____ yellow flowers

Have pairs of children choose tools to use to solve the problem and draw
to show their work.

© Houghton Mifflin Harcourt Publishing Company • Image Credits: ©Quang Ho/Shutterstock

Build Understanding

7 kites are in the sky.
The rest are on the ground.
There are 11 kites altogether.
How many kites are on the ground?

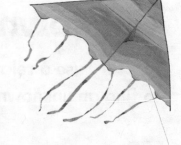

$7 +$ ▊ $= 11$

A How can you show the problem?

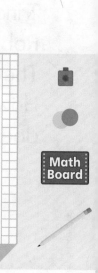

Math Board

B How can you subtract to solve the problem?

_____ – _____ = _____

C How can you use the subtraction fact
to find the unknown **addend**?

$7 +$ _____ $= 11$

D There are _____ kites on the ground.

 Turn and Talk How does using subtraction
help you find an unknown addend?

© Houghton Mifflin Harcourt Publishing Company • Image Credits: ©Ivan Gusev/Adobe Stock

Step It Out

1 9 owls in a park are small.
The rest are big.
There are 12 owls in all.
How many big owls are in the park?

$9 + \boxed{} = 12$

A Subtract the number of small owls
from the total number of owls.

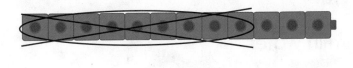

_____ – _____ = _____

B Use the subtraction fact to help you
find the unknown addend.

$9 + \underline{} = 12$

C There are _____ big owls in the park.

Check Understanding

Use subtraction to find the unknown addend.

1 9 boys wear blue.
The rest wear red.
There are 16 boys in all.
How many boys wear red?

_____ – _____ = _____

$9 + \underline{} = 16$

_____ boys wear red.

Module 4 • Lesson 5

one hundred thirty-one 131

On Your Own

Use subtraction to find the unknown addend.

2 9 penguins walk on ice.
The rest of them swim in water.
There are 14 penguins in all.
How many penguins swim in water?

$9 + \boxed{} = 14$

_____ – _____ = _____

9 + _____ = 14

_____ penguins swim in water.

---

3 Solve $8 + \boxed{} = 12$.

_____ – _____ = _____

8 + _____ = 12

4 Solve $6 + \boxed{} = 15$.

_____ – _____ = _____

6 + _____ = 15

---

5 Solve $8 + \boxed{} = 11$.

_____ – _____ = _____

8 + _____ = 11

6 Solve $7 + \boxed{} = 14$.

_____ – _____ = _____

7 + _____ = 14

⬡ I'm in a Learning Mindset!

How do children in my class use subtraction
to find an unknown addend?

_____

© Houghton Mifflin Harcourt Publishing Company • Image Credits: ©Silvia Pascual/Adobe Stock

Name _____

Solve for the Unknown Addend

(I Can) solve problems that have
an unknown addend.

Step It Out

1 ▶ 5 fish are orange.
The rest are green.
There are 14 fish in all.
How many fish are green?

$5 + \boxed{} = 14$

A Write a related subtraction fact.
Subtract the number of orange fish
from the total number of fish.

_____ – _____ = _____

B Use the subtraction fact to help you
find the unknown addend.

$14 - 5 =$ _____

So, $5 +$ _____ $= 14$.

C _____ fish are green.

Step It Out

2 Julia has 8 apples. The rest of her fruits are peaches. She has 17 fruits in all. How many peaches does Julia have?

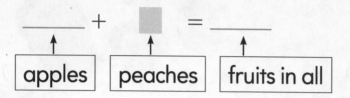

A Use addition to show the problem.

_____ + ▢ = _____
↑   ↑   ↑

| apples | peaches | fruits in all |

B Write a related subtraction fact to solve.

_____ – _____ = _____

So, 8 + _____ = 17.

C Julia has _____ peaches.

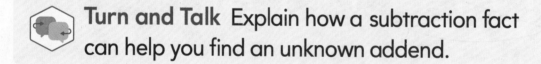

Turn and Talk Explain how a subtraction fact can help you find an unknown addend.

Check Understanding Math Board

Write a related subtraction fact to solve.

1 8 pens are blue. The rest are red. There are 14 in all. How many pens are red?

8 + ▢ = 14

_____ – _____ = _____

8 + _____ = 14

_____ red pens

On Your Own

Write a related subtraction fact to solve.

2 (MP) **Reason** 5 cows are in a field.
The rest are in a barn.
There are 12 cows in all.
How many cows are in the barn?

$5 +$ ▢ $= 12$

_____ − _____ = _____

$5 \quad +$ _____ $= \quad 12$

_____ cows are in the barn.

Explain your thinking.

_____

_____

3 9 people vote at city hall.
The rest of them vote at school.
15 people vote altogether.
How many people vote at school?

$9 +$ ▢ $= 15$

_____ − _____ = _____

$9 \quad +$ _____ $= \quad 15$

_____ people vote at school.

On Your Own

Write a related subtraction fact to solve.

4 3 bears have hats. The rest have bows.
There are 11 bears in all.
How many bears have bows?

$3 + \boxed{} = 11$

_____ − _____ = _____

3   + _____ =   11   _____ bears

---

5 (MP) **Reason** 9 dolls wear pants. The rest
wear dresses. There are 18 dolls in all.
How many dolls wear dresses?

_____ − _____ = _____

9   + _____ =   18   _____ dolls

---

6 What is $8 + \boxed{} = 17$?

_____ − _____ = _____

8   + _____ =   17

7 What is $4 + \boxed{} = 12$?

_____ − _____ = _____

4   + _____ =   12

---

8 What is $7 + \boxed{} = 14$?

_____ − _____ = _____

7   + _____ =   14

9 What is $8 + \boxed{} = 15$?

_____ − _____ = _____

8   + _____ =   15

© Houghton Mifflin Harcourt Publishing Company • Image Credits: ©Jon Helgason/Alamy

Name

Develop Fluency in Subtraction

(I Can) quickly solve subtraction facts
within 10.

Step It Out

I ▸ Annie has 8 flowers.
She wants to give some to Grace
and the rest to Marco.
What are two ways Annie
can give her flowers away?

A Think of a way to subtract from 8.
Draw and write to show your thinking.

8 – _____ = _____

_____ flowers to Grace

_____ flowers to Marco

- -

B Think of another way to subtract from 8.
Draw and write to show your thinking.

8 – _____ = _____

_____ flowers to Grace

_____ flowers to Marco

Step It Out

2 Write three ways to subtract from 7.

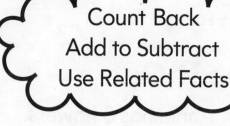

Count Back
Add to Subtract
Use Related Facts

A Think of strategies you can use.

B Write your ways.

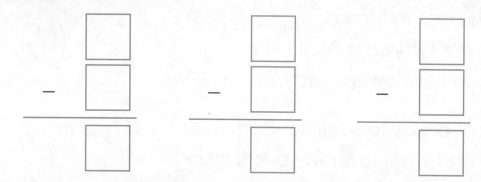

 Turn and Talk Why do the subtraction problems above start with the total on top?

Check Understanding [Math Board]

Write a subtraction equation to solve.

1 There are 9 bees. Then 2 fly away. How many bees are there now?

_____ − _____ = _____

_____ bees

Subtract. Write the difference.

2 6 − 1 = _____   **3** _____ = 10 − 2   **4** 8 − 8 = _____

On Your Own

Write a subtraction equation to solve.

5 (MP) **Model with Mathematics**
7 horses are in a field.
4 are brown. The rest are white.
How many horses are white?

_____ – _____ = _____

_____ white horses

6 **Open Ended** Write two subtraction
equations that use the same three numbers.

_____ – _____ = _____

_____ – _____ = _____

Subtract. Write the difference.

7 $3 - 3 =$ _____	**8** $8 - 7 =$ _____	**9** _____ $= 10 - 1$
10 _____ $= 10 - 0$	**11** $3 - 2 =$ _____	**12** $7 - 5 =$ _____
13 _____ $= 5 - 3$	**14** _____ $= 10 - 8$	**15** $9 - 3 =$ _____
16 _____ $= 8 - 4$	**17** $6 - 2 =$ _____	**18** _____ $= 9 - 8$

On Your Own

Subtract to solve.

19 (MP) **Model with Mathematics**
9 fire trucks are at the station.
Then 5 fire trucks leave.
How many fire trucks are
at the station now?

$$\begin{array}{r} \square \\ - \ \square \\ \hline \square \end{array}$$

_____ fire trucks

Subtract. Write the difference.

20
$$\begin{array}{r} 5 \\ - \ 3 \\ \hline \square \end{array}$$

21
$$\begin{array}{r} 4 \\ - \ 3 \\ \hline \square \end{array}$$

22
$$\begin{array}{r} 9 \\ - \ 4 \\ \hline \square \end{array}$$

23
$$\begin{array}{r} 10 \\ - \ 7 \\ \hline \square \end{array}$$

24
$$\begin{array}{r} 7 \\ - \ 0 \\ \hline \square \end{array}$$

25
$$\begin{array}{r} 8 \\ - \ 3 \\ \hline \square \end{array}$$

26
$$\begin{array}{r} 7 \\ - \ 6 \\ \hline \square \end{array}$$

27
$$\begin{array}{r} 10 \\ - \ 7 \\ \hline \square \end{array}$$

28
$$\begin{array}{r} 9 \\ - \ 1 \\ \hline \square \end{array}$$

29
$$\begin{array}{r} 7 \\ - \ 3 \\ \hline \square \end{array}$$

30
$$\begin{array}{r} 8 \\ - \ 2 \\ \hline \square \end{array}$$

31
$$\begin{array}{r} 10 \\ - \ 5 \\ \hline \square \end{array}$$

Keep Going to▶ Practice and Homework Journal

Name _____

Review

Concepts and Skill

Solve. Then circle the pairs that are related facts.

1 $6 + 5 =$ _____

$11 - 5 =$ _____

2 $3 + 8 =$ _____

$8 - 3 =$ _____

3 $5 + 7 =$ _____

$7 - 5 =$ _____

4 $9 + 6 =$ _____

$15 - 9 =$ _____

Complete the related facts.
Use 🔲🔲 if you need to.

5 $5 + 9 =$ _____

$9 +$ _____ $= 14$

$14 - 9 =$ _____

_____ $-$ _____ $=$ _____

Write an addition equation to help you subtract.

6 What is $12 - 4$?

_____ $+$ _____ $=$ _____

So, $12 - 4 =$ _____.

7 What is $16 - 9$?

_____ $+$ _____ $=$ _____

So, $16 - 9 =$ _____.

Use subtraction to find the unknown addend.

8 Solve $7 + \boxed{} = 16$.

$\underline{} - \underline{} = \underline{}$

$7 + \underline{} = 16$

Write a related subtraction fact to solve.

9 Teresa has 8 yellow flowers.
The rest of her flowers are red.
She has 14 flowers altogether.
How many red flowers does she have?

$8 + \boxed{} = 14$

$\underline{} - \underline{} = \underline{}$

$8 + \underline{} = 14$　　　　$\underline{}$ red flowers

Fill in the bubble next to the correct answer.

10 Which is the difference?　　$\begin{array}{r} 8 \\ -\ 3 \\ \hline \end{array}$

　○ 5　　　　　　　○ 6　　　　　　　○ 11

11 Which addition equation can be used
to check the answer to $15 - 7 = \boxed{}$?

　○ $7 + 1 = 8$　　　○ $6 + 9 = 15$　　　○ $7 + 8 = 15$